ACTIVITY PHONICS

by Betty Pollard

World Teachers Press

Order Number 2-5034
ISBN 1-885111-47-9
E F G H 04 03 02 01

Educational Resources

395 Main Street
Rowley, MA 01969

ACTIVITY PHONICS

Introduction

This book is a large selection of activities based on the phonetic sounds of the English language. It is intended that the activities be used as an integral part of early teaching programs and that you will use the worksheets and the ideas on each page to help to introduce, teach or consolidate the basic sounds, depending on the needs of your class or of individuals within the class.

The activities are consistent throughout the book to allow for ease of use, and aim to consolidate and extend the vocabulary of young children. The activities also allow for a variety of teaching strategies, including whole-class, group and individual activities.

Contents

Teacher Information

Introduction

Activity Phonics is a series of blackline masters that focuses on introducing phonic sounds. As new sounds are introduced the activities in these books provide a specific focus on individual sounds. As students develop an understanding of the sound they are then able to complete more difficult activities that present the sound in context, imbedded in text.

The presentation and layout of each sound is deliberately similar. This ensures that the student is working on the sound being introduced and not absorbed in comprehending peripheral issues associated with page layout. It also allows for independent work by individuals who have experience working with this format.

Teachers can use the activities in this series in a variety of ways including:

(i)   whole class application when new sounds are being introduced.

(ii)   as revision of sounds.

(iii)   remedial work for students who are having difficulty with basic phonic sounds.

(iv)   extension work where the second activity in each pair is given to those students who demonstrate a good understanding.

Phonic Activities

In addition to the activities found in this series, the following activities can be used with each phonic sound to introduce, consolidate and extend knowledge.

- Construct booklets which display pictures with words containing the sound being treated.
- Sort selected pictures and words into sound groups.
- Locate words containing the sound within set passages or encourage students to locate the sound in their reading.
- Construct individual sound dictionaries with students.
- Ask students to create rhyming pairs for words with the same phonic sound.

- Use the phonic sound to build a word bank which can be displayed and added to as students discover new words with the same phonic sound.
- Display messages around the classroom which highlight the phonic sound being treated.
- Write letters to students which highlight particular phonic sounds.
- Sort words into common visual/sound pages.

Teacher Information
Example lesson Development

Activity

'y' as in sky - page 6.

Introductory Work

Introducing new sounds to students is very important in the formation of early literacy skills. Students will have used most sounds in oral communication and now need to relate this oral usage to the written form. Therefore introductory activities need to start in the oral form working on the foundation that already exists. Ask students to provide their own examples of words with the specific sound, use pictures which show words with the sound in use.

With the oral work it is vital that the correct pronounciation is used. Misconceptions developed at the early stage will be very difficult to alter later on. Repetition of the sound and words containing the sound will assist in this area.

Completing the Worksheets

Each sound is supported by an activity sheet(s), that identifies words containing the sound and applies the words in simple language activities.

1. Introduce the sound through oral activities.

2. Use the words containing the phonic sound in a meaningful context.

3. Word-building activities to devlop a word bank with students.

5. See page 4 for further follow up activities

4. Comprehension to ensure students have an understanding of the words being dealt with.

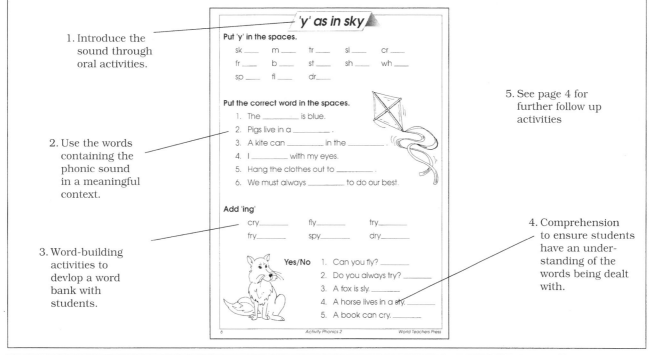

'y' as in sky

Put 'y' in the spaces.

sk ___   m ___   tr ___   sl ___   cr ___
fr ___   b ___   st ___   sh ___   wh ___
sp ___   fl ___   dr ___

Put the correct word in the spaces.
1. The _____ is blue.
2. Pigs live in a _____ .
3. A kite can _____ in the _____ .
4. I _____ with my eyes.
5. Hang the clothes out to _____ .
6. We must always _____ to do our best.

Add 'ing'
cry_____   fly_____   try_____
fry_____   spy_____   dry_____

Yes/No   1. Can you fly? _____
2. Do you always try? _____
3. A fox is sly. _____
4. A horse lives in a sty. _____
5. A book can cry. _____

6   Activity Phonics 2   World Teachers Press

Extension

Extension activities should focus on identifying more words containing the particular sound and then using the words in practical activities such as writing short sentences and 'read and draw'.

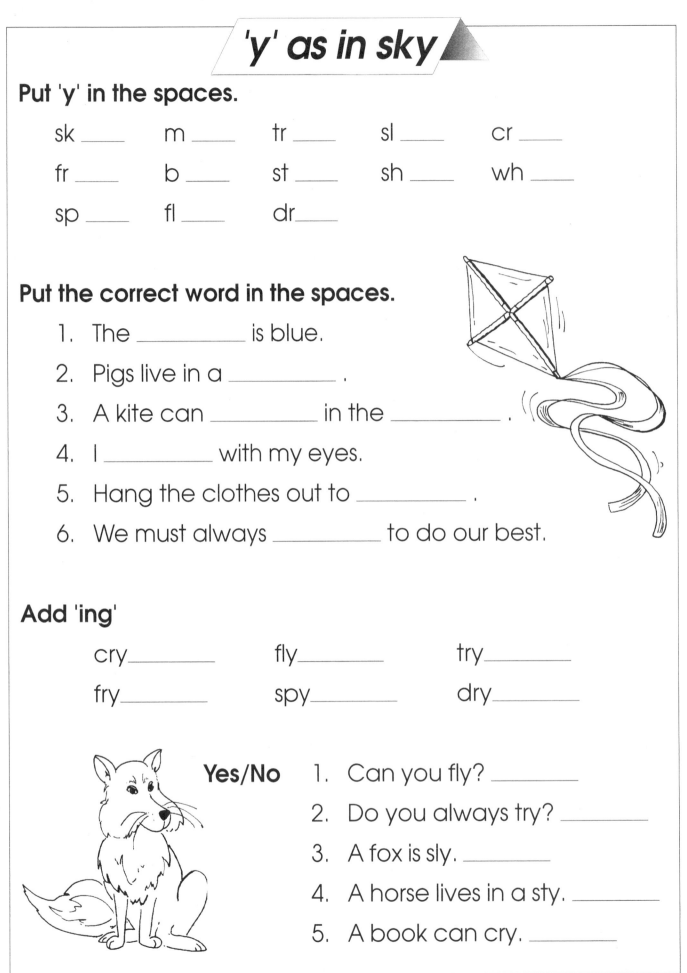

'y' as in sky

Put 'y' in the spaces.

sk ___   m ___   tr ___   sl ___   cr ___

fr ___   b ___   st ___   sh ___   wh ___

sp ___   fl ___   dr___

Put the correct word in the spaces.

1. The _____ is blue.

2. Pigs live in a _____ .

3. A kite can _____ in the _____ .

4. I _____ with my eyes.

5. Hang the clothes out to _____ .

6. We must always _____ to do our best.

Add 'ing'

cry_____   fly_____   try_____

fry_____   spy_____   dry_____

Yes/No

1. Can you fly? _____

2. Do you always try? _____

3. A fox is sly. _____

4. A horse lives in a sty. _____

5. A book can cry. _____

'y' as in teddy

Put 'y' in the spaces.

tedd ____   bab ____   jell ____   kitt ____

pupp ____   lad ____   joll ____   spott ____

happ ____   bump ____   smell ____   gust ____

rust ____   wind ____   sunn ____

rain ____   cloud ____   funn ____

Yes/No

1. Have you seen a spotty frog? _____

2. Have you seen a rusty nail? _____

3. Have you been on a bumpy road? _____

4. Have you seen a funny clown? _____

5. Have you picked up a puppy? _____

6. Is it windy today? _____

7. Is it sunny today? _____

8. Is it cloudy today? _____

Read and draw.

A happy teddy
having a picnic on
a sunny day.

'll' as in hill

Put 'll' in the spaces.

hi____   be____   do____   bi____

se____   ro____   fi____   we____

Po____y   ki____   fe____   do____y

mi____   te____   du____   ti____

spe____   wi____   sme____   gu____

spi____   swe____

Put in the correct words.

1. Jack and Jill went up the _____ .

2. Do not _____ the milk.

3. We saw a _____ at the beach.

4. We _____ with our nose.

5. _____ is a parrot.

6. A duck has a _____ .

7. At the farm we saw a wind_____ .

8. Our teacher will _____ us a story.

9. I had a pastrami _____ for lunch.

Read and draw.

A windmill

on a farm.

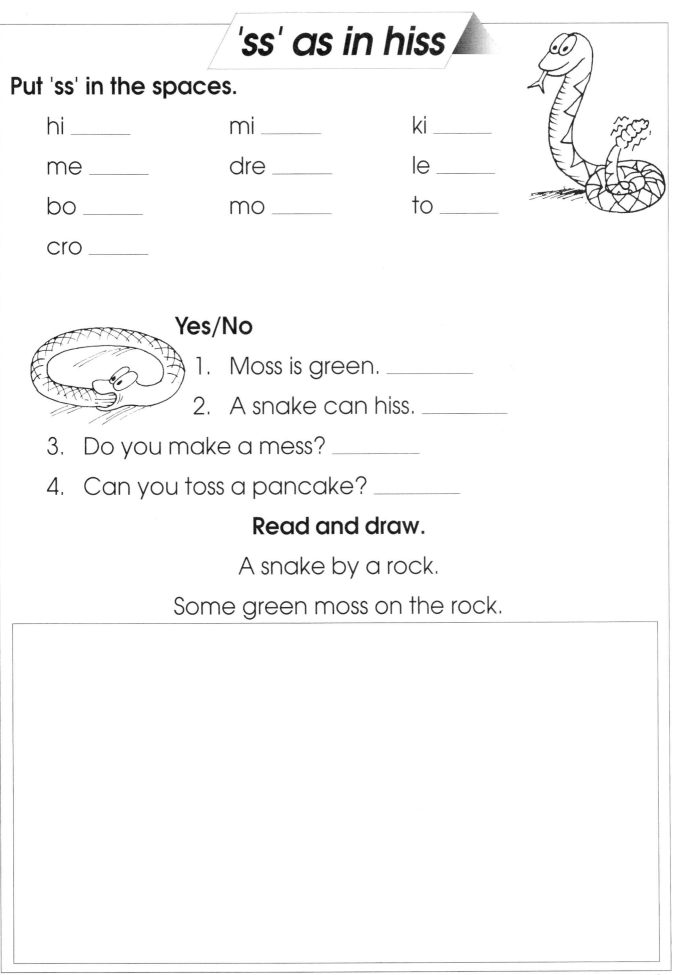

'ss' as in hiss

Put 'ss' in the spaces.

hi _____   mi _____   ki _____

me _____   dre _____   le _____

bo _____   mo _____   to _____

cro _____

Yes/No

1. Moss is green. _____

2. A snake can hiss. _____

3. Do you make a mess? _____

4. Can you toss a pancake? _____

Read and draw.

A snake by a rock.

Some green moss on the rock.

'e' as in me

Put 'e' in the spaces.

h ____   m ____   w ____   b ____   sh ____

Put in the correct words.

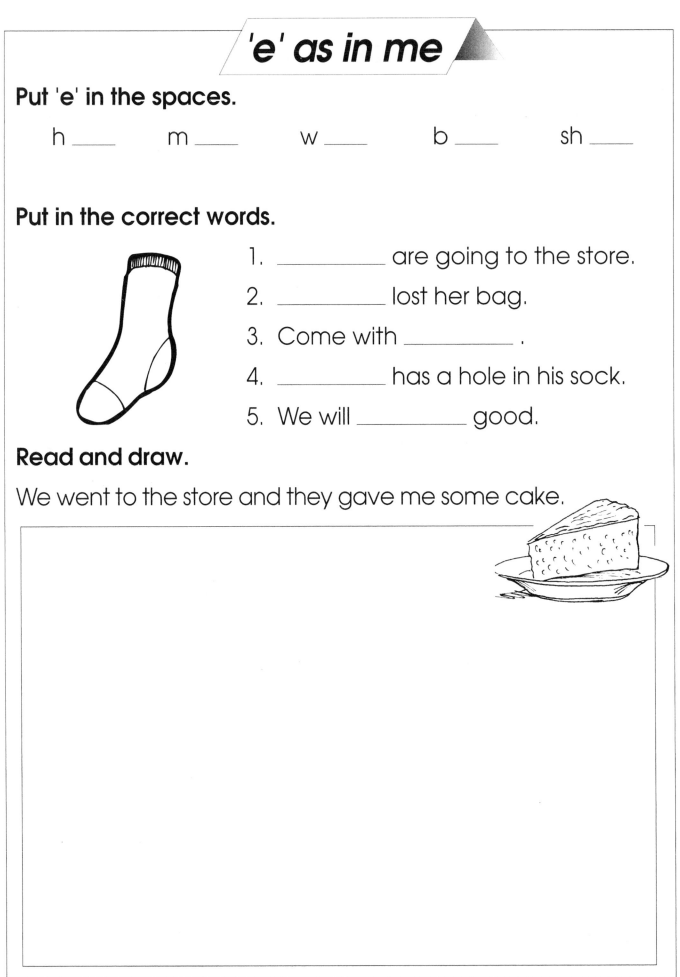

1. _____ are going to the store.

2. _____ lost her bag.

3. Come with _____ .

4. _____ has a hole in his sock.

5. We will _____ good.

Read and draw.

We went to the store and they gave me some cake.

'ck' as in duck

Put 'ck' in the spaces.

du _____   Ja _____   si _____   ki _____

sa _____   ba _____   li _____   ro _____

chi _____   lo _____   bri _____   tri _____

clo _____   so _____   ne _____   pe _____

pa _____   ro _____ et   po _____ et

ti _____ –to _____

Put in the missing words.

1. The clock went _____–_____ .

2. Put the _____ with the shoe.

3. _____ and Jill went up the hill.

4. The mother _____ has a duckling.

5. The _____ went up into the sky.

6. We can _____ a football.

Read and draw.

A Mother Duck and her ducklings swimming on the pond.

'tr' as in tree

Put 'tr' in the spaces.

_____ ee	_____ ay	_____ ousers	_____ easure
_____ acks	_____ ick	_____ ip	_____ iangle
_____ ickle	_____ uck	_____ y	_____ ap

Put in the missing words.

1. The pirates had some _____ .

2. A clown can do a _____ .

3. A train goes on railroad _____ .

4. The _____ was blown over in the storm.

Read and draw.

A big tree and
a little tree.

A garden near
the trees.

Yes/No

Do you like trees? _____ Are trees important? _____

'pr' as in pretty

Put 'pr' in the spaces.

_____ ice   _____ ess   _____ esent

_____ int   _____ ay   _____ etty

_____ incess   _____ opeller   _____ ize

Put in the missing words.

1. Did you win a _____ .

2. A _____ lives in a castle.

3. A boat has a _____ .

4. My birthday _____ was a new bike.

5. The baby is very _____ .

Read and draw.

A castle. A princess in the castle. The king and queen.

'fr' as in frog

Put 'fr' in the spaces.

_____ og _____ ee _____ iend _____ uit

_____ y _____ ying _____ om _____ ame

_____ ight _____ ost _____ eckles

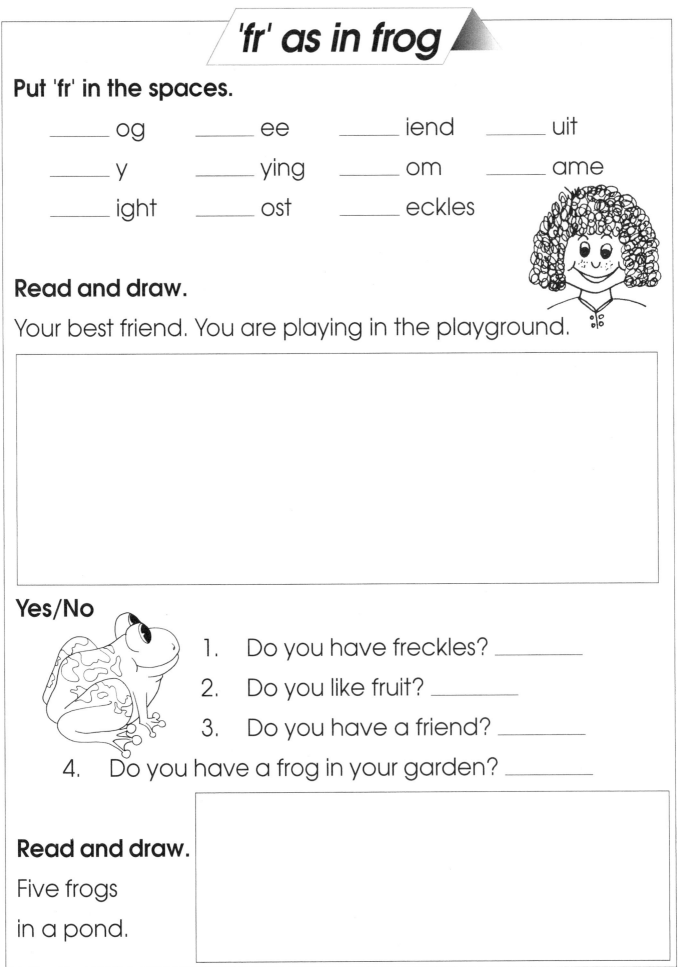

Read and draw.

Your best friend. You are playing in the playground.

Yes/No

1. Do you have freckles? _____

2. Do you like fruit? _____

3. Do you have a friend? _____

4. Do you have a frog in your garden? _____

Read and draw.

Five frogs

in a pond.

'br' as in brown

Put 'br' in the spaces.

_____ own   _____ icks   _____ idge   _____ ush

_____ ushes   _____ ead   _____ oom   _____ other

_____ eak   _____ ing   _____ im   _____ ide

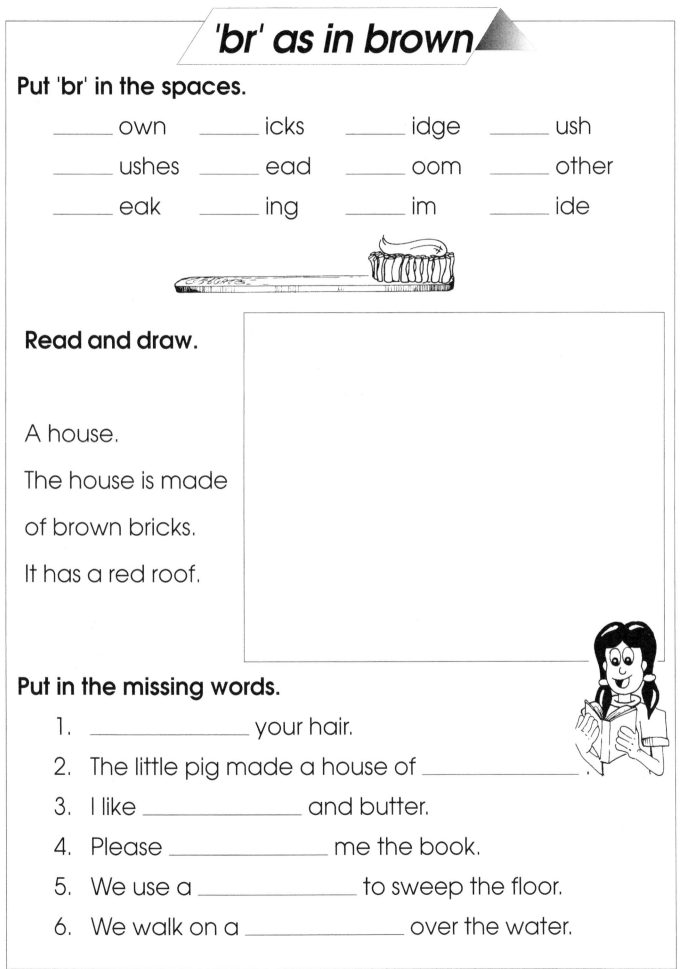

Read and draw.

A house.

The house is made

of brown bricks.

It has a red roof.

Put in the missing words.

1. _____ your hair.

2. The little pig made a house of _____ .

3. I like _____ and butter.

4. Please _____ me the book.

5. We use a _____ to sweep the floor.

6. We walk on a _____ over the water.

'cr' as in crab

Put 'cr' in the spaces.

_____ ab	_____ oss	_____ awl	_____ ash
_____ own	_____ eam	_____ ackers	_____ ane
_____ ayons	_____ icket	_____ ust	_____ eep

Put in the missing word.

1. There is a _____ in the grass.

2. I color with _____ .

3. I like cheese and _____ .

4. The baby can _____ .

5. Two cars were in a _____ .

Read and draw.

A crab. The crab has a crown.

A dish of crackers.

Yes /No

1. Do you like crackers? _____

2. Do you like the crust on bread? _____

'dr' as in drum

Put 'dr' in the spaces.

_____ um   _____ ink   _____ op   _____ ess

_____ aw   _____ agon   _____ ive   _____ eam

Yes/No

1. Have you seen a dragon? _____

2. Do you have a drum? _____

3. Can you drive a car? _____

Draw a dragon with a drum.

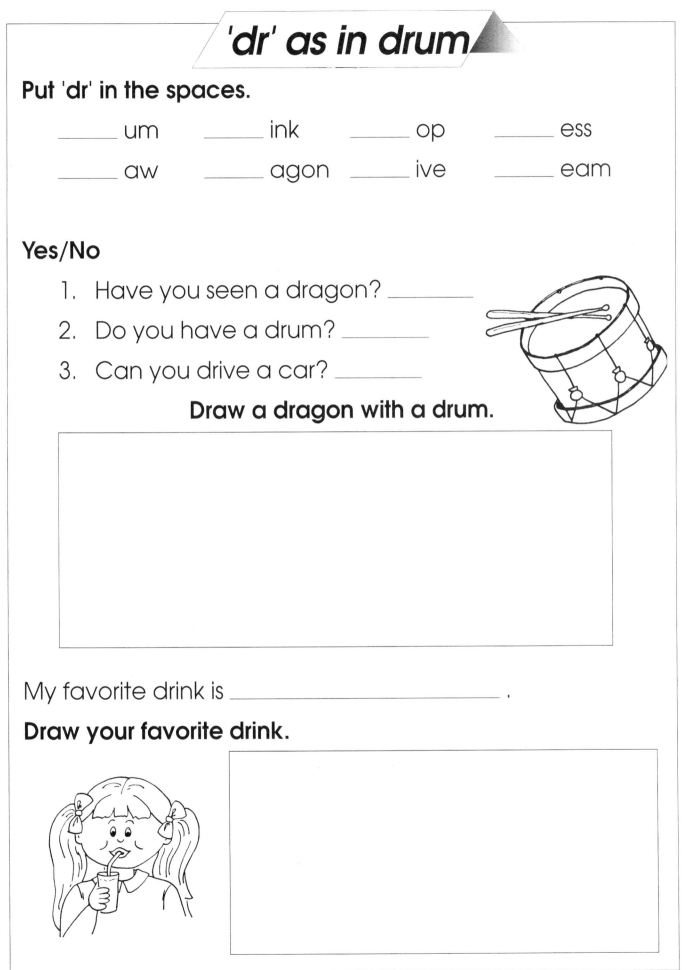

My favorite drink is _____ .

Draw your favorite drink.

'gr' as in grow

Put 'gr' in the spaces.

_____ ow   _____ ass   _____ and

_____ een   _____ apes   _____ ill

_____ ay   _____ ab   _____ andmother

_____ andfather

Yes/No

1. Do you have a grandmother? _____

2. Do you have a grandfather? _____

3. Do you like grapes? _____

4. Is grass green? _____

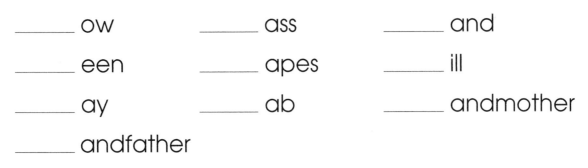

Read and draw.

Grandmother and Grandfather are sitting in the garden.

They are eating grapes.

'gl' as in glad

Put 'gl' in the spaces.

_____ ad   _____ ow   _____ ass

_____ ue   _____ itter   _____ asses

_____ ider   _____ obe   _____ oves

Yes/No

1. Have you seen a glider? _____

2. Do you have some glue? _____

3. Are you glad to be in school? _____

4. Do you have some gloves? _____

5. Have you seen a globe? _____

6. Do you wear glasses? _____

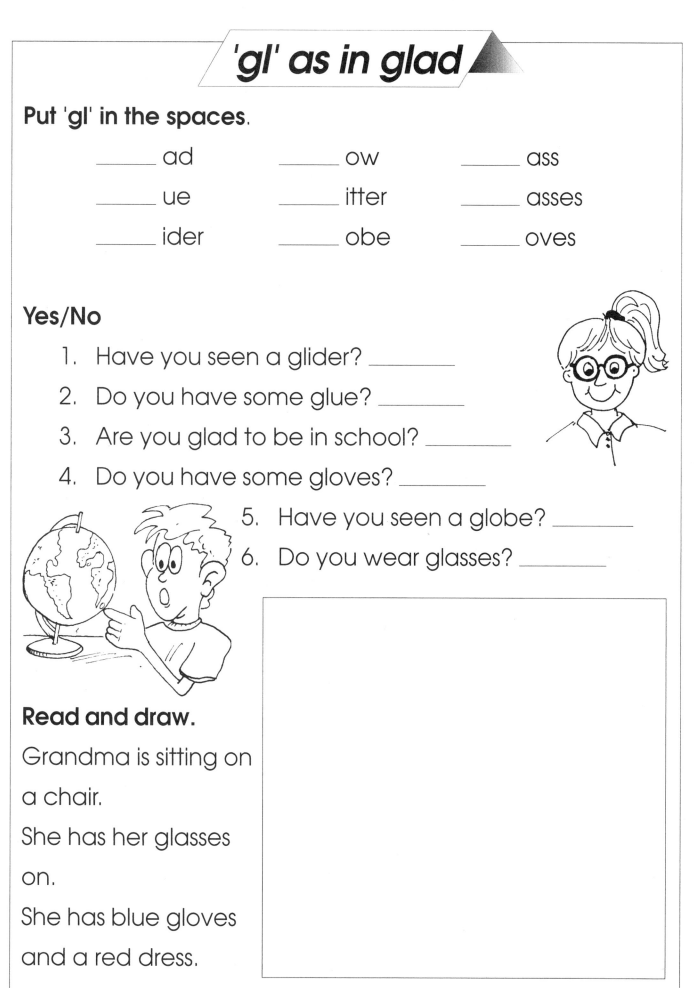

Read and draw.

Grandma is sitting on
a chair.

She has her glasses
on.

She has blue gloves
and a red dress.

'sl' as in slide

Put 'sl' in the spaces.

_____ ide   _____ am   _____ ippers

_____ ip   _____ ow   _____ eep

_____ ed   _____ eeve   _____ ice

Put in the correct words.

1. We went down the _____ .

2. I _____ in a bed.

3. Mother has some new _____ .

4. Do not _____ on the wet floor.

Yes/No

1. Would you like a slice of bread? _____

2. Have you been on a sled? _____

3. Did you slam the door? _____

4. Can you slice a cake? _____

Read and draw.

Two children on a sled.   A slice of cake.

'pl' as in play

Put 'pl' in the spaces.

_____ay   _____um   _____ant

_____ug   _____ate   _____atypus

_____us   _____ane   _____anet

_____an   _____ayground

Read and draw.

Some children playing in the playground.

A plane in the sky.

A plum on a plate.
The plum is purple.

'bl' as in black

Put 'bl' in the spaces.

_____ ack   _____ ue   _____ ock   _____ anket

_____ end   _____ ade   _____ ossoms

_____ ood   _____ ister   _____ ow

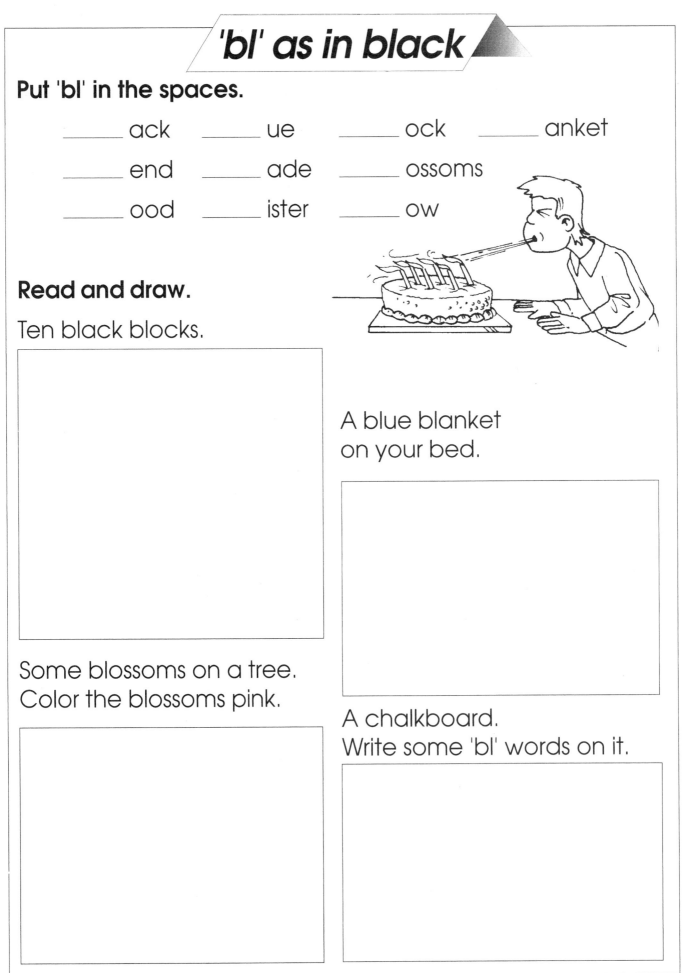

Read and draw.

Ten black blocks.

A blue blanket
on your bed.

Some blossoms on a tree.
Color the blossoms pink.

A chalkboard.
Write some 'bl' words on it.

Activity Phonics   *World Teachers Press*

Put 'fl' in the spaces.

_____ ag	_____ oss	_____ owers	_____ ew
_____ at	_____ ower	_____ our	_____ oor
_____ ames	_____ ash	_____ ock	_____ ed
_____ ee	_____ y	_____ ies	_____ ap
_____ ight			

Read and draw.

A flash of lightning in the sky.

A flock of sheep on a farm.

A car with a flat tire.

'cl' as in clown

Put 'cl' in the spaces.

_____ own   _____ iff   _____ ap   _____ oud

_____ am   _____ imb   _____ ock   _____ aws

_____ ogs   _____ assroom

Yes/No

1. A clown can clap. _____
2. Can you climb up the stairs? _____
3. A clock can clap. _____
4. Clogs are shoes. _____
5. A clock goes click-clack. _____

Read and draw.

Some people standing on top of a cliff.

A clown clapping his hands.

'ing' as in ring

Put 'ing' in the spaces.

r _____   s _____   k _____   noth _____

fl _____   th _____   cl _____   morn _____

sw _____   br _____   spr _____   str _____

st _____   w _____

Put in the missing words.

1. Mother wears a _____ on her finger.

2. The _____ has a crown.

3. The bird hurt its _____ .

4. I like to play on the _____ .

5. Please _____ me my book.

6. Every _____ I wash my face.

7. In music class, we _____ .

8. My kitten plays with a ball of _____ .

Read and draw.

A black and white kitten playing with a ball of string.

'st' as in stop and nest

Put 'st' in the spaces.

____ op   ____ em   ____ ick   ____ ars

____ and   ____ amp   ____ ill   ____ ay

____ iff   ne ____   be ____   re ____

te ____   we ____   co ____   lo ____

mu ____   ju ____   cru ____   mi ____

Put the missing word in each space.

1. A plant has a _____ .

2. The bird sat on the _____ .

3. I always do my _____ work.

4. The boy _____ his bag.

5. _____ up.

6. The police officer said '_____'!

Yes/No

1. Have you seen mist? _____

2. Do you like crusts? _____

3. Did you have a rest? _____

4. Can you sit still? _____

5. Can you stamp your feet? _____

'sn' as in snail

Put 'sn' in the spaces.

_____ ail	_____ ap	_____ ip	_____ ow
_____ ake	_____ ack	_____ eeze	_____ owman
_____ iff	_____ ore	_____ out	_____ uggle
_____ eakers			

Put in the missing words.

1. A _____ has a shell.

2. A _____ has scales.

3. We make a _____ out of snow.

4. We wear _____ on our feet.

Read and draw.

A snowman.

He has a black hat

and a scarf.

A long snake. It is moving along the ground.

'sp' as in spot

Put 'sp' in the spaces.

_____ ot   _____ an   _____ ider   _____ ell

_____ ace   _____ end   _____ ort

_____ iny   _____ eckle   _____ oon

_____ ade   _____ in   _____ eed   _____ ill

Put in the missing words.

1. A _____ has a web.

2. Do not _____ your drink.

3. We can _____ words.

4. We dig in the garden with a _____ .

5. We eat soup with a _____ .

6. Do not _____ in your car.

Read and draw.

A spider
in a web.

A rocket
in space.

'sm' as in smell

Put 'sm' in the spaces.

_____ ell   _____ all   _____ ash   _____ ile

_____ oke   _____ ock   _____ udge   _____ art

_____ og

Yes/No

1. Are you small? _____
2. Can you smile? _____
3. Can you smell? _____
4. Do you like smog? _____

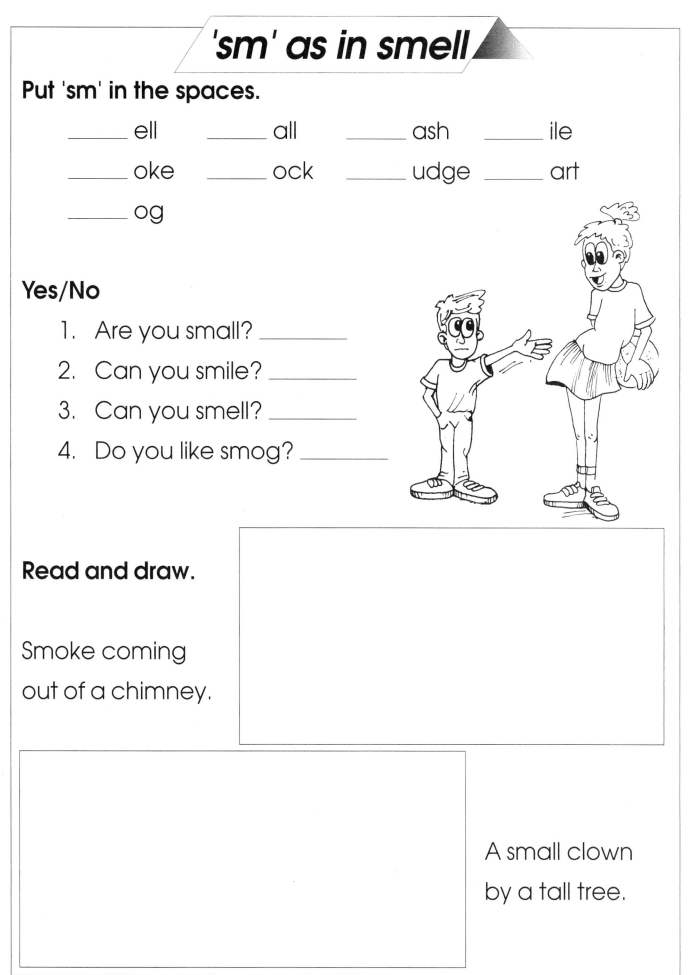

Read and draw.

Smoke coming
out of a chimney.

A small clown
by a tall tree.

'sw' as in swim

Put 'sw' in the spaces.

_____ im   _____ ing   _____ eep   _____ itch

_____ eet   _____ allow   _____ an   _____ eets

_____ oop   _____ imming

Yes/No

1. Do you like sweets? _____

2. Can you swim? _____

3. Do you like swimming? _____

4. Have you seen a swan? _____

5. Do you like playing on a swing? _____

6. Can a bird swoop? _____

Read and draw.

Draw a swimming pool. Lots of children are swimming.

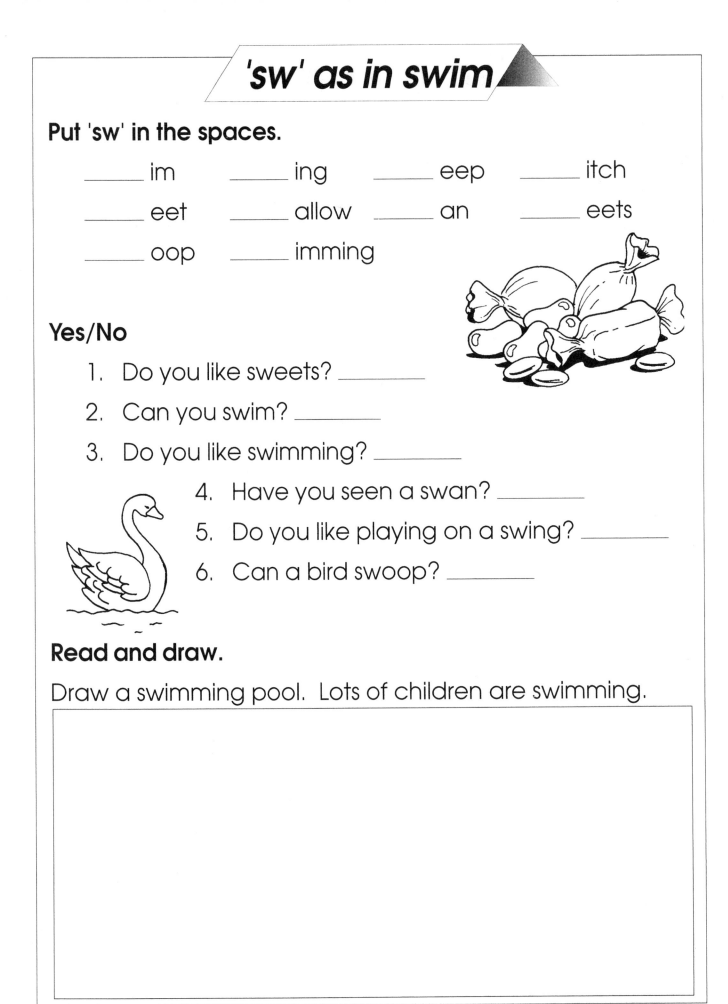

'sc' as in score

Put 'sc' in the spaces.

_____ arf   _____ out   _____ oop   _____ ooter

_____ ales   _____ an   _____ atter   _____ ar

_____ ore   _____ rape   _____ rew   _____ rub

Yes/No

1. Does a fish have scales? _____
2. Did you scrub the floor? _____
3. Can a cat scratch? _____
4. Do you have a scar? _____
5. Do you wear a scarf? _____
6. Can you ride a scooter? _____

Read and draw.

Draw yourself riding a scooter. You have a scarf around your neck.

'sk' as in skip and tusk

Put 'sk' in the spaces.

_____ y   _____ in   _____ ip   _____ ipping

_____ irt   _____ i   _____ ill   _____ eleton

_____ ull   _____ ate   tu _____

hu _____   ri _____   de _____

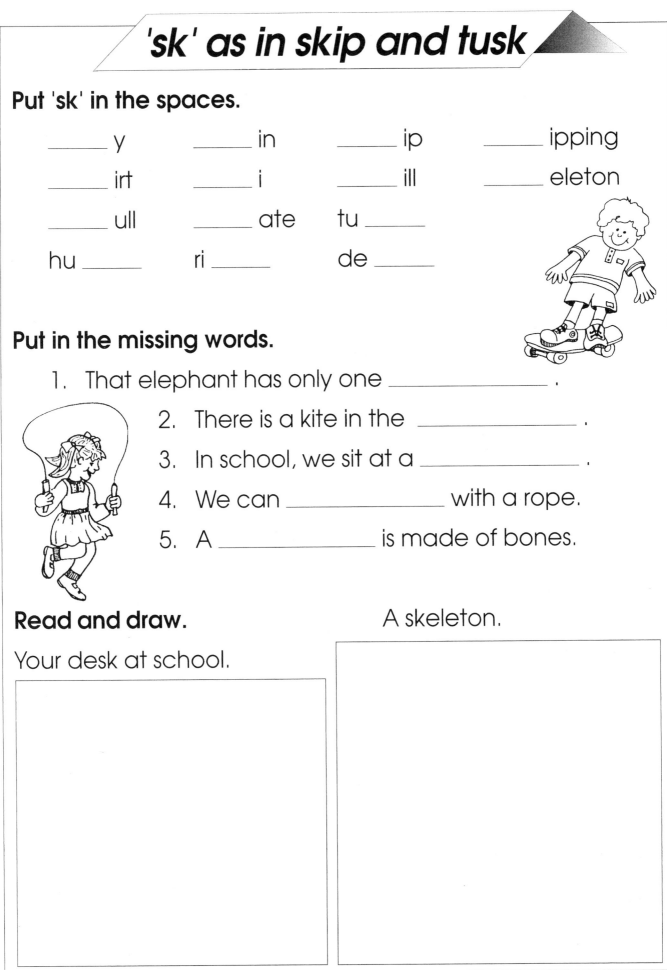

Put in the missing words.

1. That elephant has only one _____ .

2. There is a kite in the _____ .

3. In school, we sit at a _____ .

4. We can _____ with a rope.

5. A _____ is made of bones.

Read and draw.

Your desk at school.

A skeleton.

'ch' as in chick and lunch

Put 'ch' in the spaces.

_____ ick	_____ op	_____ ip	_____ ur _____
_____ at	_____ est	_____ ill	_____ ildren
_____ air	_____ in	_____ eck	_____ imney
mu _____	su _____	pin _____	_____ eese
pun _____	lun _____	ri _____	mar _____

Put in the missing words.

1. Please sit in the _____ .

2. We had _____ sandwiches for _____.

3. Please _____ the wood for the fire.

4. The wolf fell down the _____.

5. On Sunday we go to _____.

6. A _____ says cheep, cheep.

Read and draw.

Two children. They have ten chicks in a box.

'sh' as in ship and wish

Put 'sh' in the spaces.

_____ ip   _____ ell   _____ ut   _____ ed

_____ eep   _____ oe   _____ ark   _____ arp

_____ elf   _____ e   _____ op   fi _____

wi _____   sma _____   fla _____   cra _____

fre _____   bru _____

Put in the missing words.

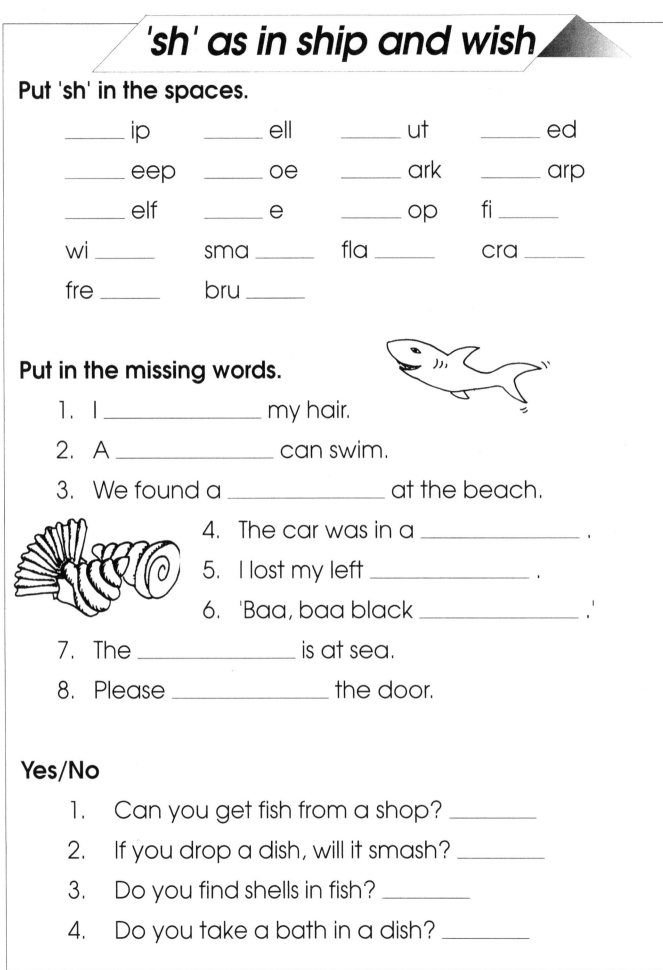

1. I _____ my hair.

2. A _____ can swim.

3. We found a _____ at the beach.

   4. The car was in a _____ .

   5. I lost my left _____ .

   6. 'Baa, baa black _____ .'

7. The _____ is at sea.

8. Please _____ the door.

Yes/No

1. Can you get fish from a shop? _____

2. If you drop a dish, will it smash? _____

3. Do you find shells in fish? _____

4. Do you take a bath in a dish? _____

'th' as in three and bath

Put 'th' in the spaces.

_____ ree   _____ is   _____ en   _____ an

_____ imble   _____ em   _____ ick   _____ at

_____ umb   _____ in   _____ e   _____ under

ba _____   mo _____   tee _____   pa _____

clo _____   mou _____   ba _____ tub

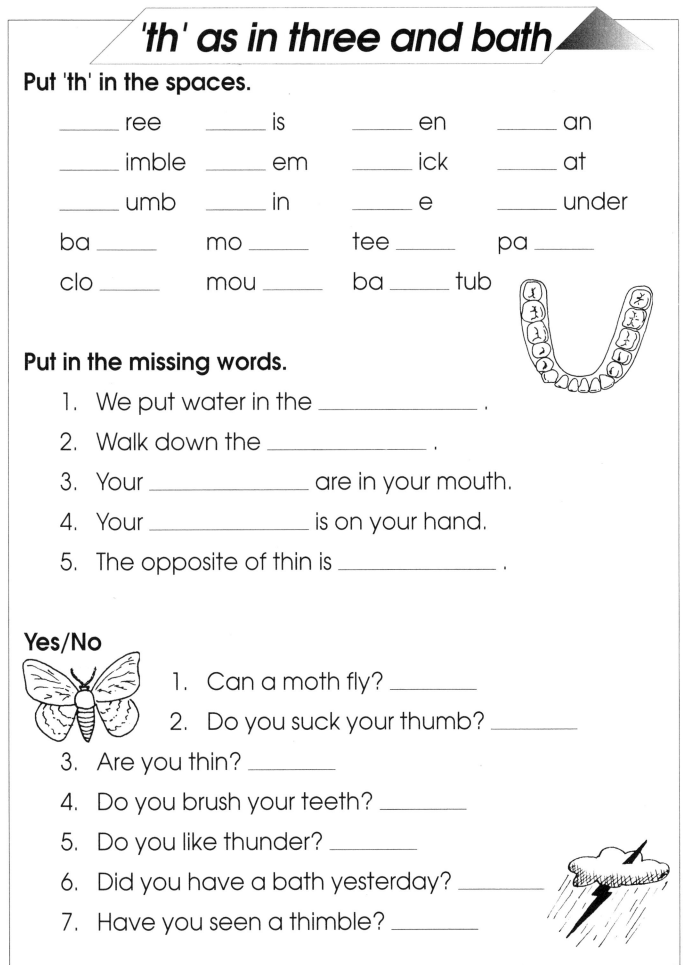

Put in the missing words.

1. We put water in the _____ .

2. Walk down the _____ .

3. Your _____ are in your mouth.

4. Your _____ is on your hand.

5. The opposite of thin is _____ .

Yes/No

1. Can a moth fly? _____

2. Do you suck your thumb? _____

3. Are you thin? _____

4. Do you brush your teeth? _____

5. Do you like thunder? _____

6. Did you have a bath yesterday? _____

7. Have you seen a thimble? _____

'wh' as in whip

Put 'wh' in the spaces.

_____ ip	_____ y	_____ en	_____ at
_____ ale	_____ eel	_____ ite	_____ eat
_____ ere	_____ ile	_____ iskers	_____ istle

Put in the missing words.

1. A _____ lives in the sea.

2. Cats have _____ .

3. A _____ is round.

4. You can blow a _____ .

5. A farmer grows _____ .

Read and draw. A whale in the sea.

'all' as in ball

Put 'all' in the spaces.

b _____   c _____   w _____   h _____

t _____   f _____   sm _____   st _____

Put in the missing words.

1. The _____ bounced up and down.

2. In the toy store there was a _____ doll.

3. Mother will _____ us for lunch.

4. A horse can sleep in a _____ .

5. Humpty Dumpty sat on a _____ .

6. The _____ man was on stilts.

7. Do not walk on the wall because you

   will _____ .

Read and draw.

Draw Humpty Dumpty sitting on the wall.

A tall man is standing by the wall.

'ee' as in tree

Put 'ee' in the spaces.

tr _____   s _____   f _____ t   cr _____ p

b _____   f _____ d   p _____ l   qu _____ n

st _____ p   fr _____   f _____ l   gr _____ n

n _____ d   s _____ k   k _____ p   sl _____ p

d _____ p   w _____ k   sw _____ p   s _____ m

w _____ p   sw _____ t   st _____ p

Yes/No

1. A tree is green. _____

2. I can peel an apple. _____

3. Cheese is green. _____

4. I sleep on my feet. _____

5. A bee can sting me. _____

Put in the missing words.

1. We _____ in a bed.

2. Some apples are _____ .

3. I will _____ my apple.

4. Apples grow on a _____ .

5. There are seven days in a _____ .

6. I put shoes on my _____ .

'ea' as in leaf

Put 'ea' in the spaces.

l ___ f   cl ___ n   b ___ ch   t ___

t ___ m   r ___ ch   s ___   ___ ch

p ___ ch   ___ t   m ___ t   t ___ cher

n ___ t   st ___ m   cr ___ m   b ___ n

h ___ t   wh ___ t   fl ___   p ___

m ___ n   r ___ d   r ___ ding

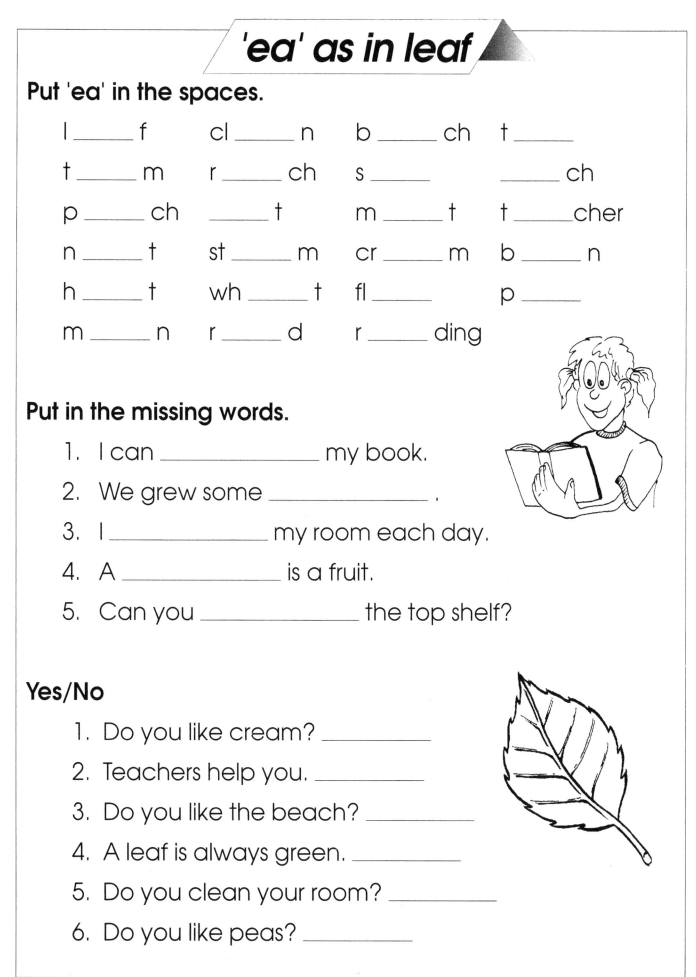

Put in the missing words.

1. I can _____ my book.

2. We grew some _____ .

3. I _____ my room each day.

4. A _____ is a fruit.

5. Can you _____ the top shelf?

Yes/No

1. Do you like cream? _____

2. Teachers help you. _____

3. Do you like the beach? _____

4. A leaf is always green. _____

5. Do you clean your room? _____

6. Do you like peas? _____

'ea' as in leaf

Put 'ea' in the spaces.

cr ___ m   wh ___ t   s ___ side

st ___ m   fl ___   b ___ ch

Put in the missing words.

1. A farmer grows _____ .

2. The _____ hopped on the dog.

3. _____ comes out of a kettle.

4. We found shells at the _____ .

5. I like bread and jam and _____ .

6. We played on the sand at the _____ .

Add 's'

teacher ___   flea ___   team ___

Add 'es'

beach ___   peach ___   reach ___

Add 'ing'

read ___   eat ___   speak ___

teach ___   clean ___   heat ___

What am I?

I have water, sand
and shells. _____

'ar' as in car

Put 'ar' in the spaces.

c _____   c _____ d   y _____ d   st _____ t

f _____   p _____ k   d _____ k   sh _____ k

st _____   t _____   b _____   c _____ pet

f _____ m   c _____ t   t _____ t   g _____ den

M _____ k   b _____ k   sh _____ p   h _____ d

Put in the missing words.

1. I saw a _____ in the sky.

2. We went to the _____ to play.

3. The car will not _____ .

4. A rock is _____ .

5. It is _____ at night.

6. _____ is a boy's name.

7. A _____ has very _____ teeth.

Read and draw.

A house.

Put a car in the yard.

Put some stars in the sky.

Make a pretty garden.

'oo' as in moon

Put 'oo' in the spaces.

m _____ n   r _____ f   br _____ m   b _____ t

sch _____ l   ball _____ n   h _____ p   kangar _____

z _____   f _____ d   sp _____ n   t _____

p _____ l   t _____ th   st _____ l   c _____ l

t _____ t   sh _____ t

Put in the missing words.

1. You eat _____ .

2. We sweep with a _____ .

3. A _____ hops.

4. A _____ floats in the air.

5. We go to _____ each day.

6. You put a _____ on a foot.

7. Our house has a _____ .

8. I lost my _____ .

9. You can swim in our _____ .

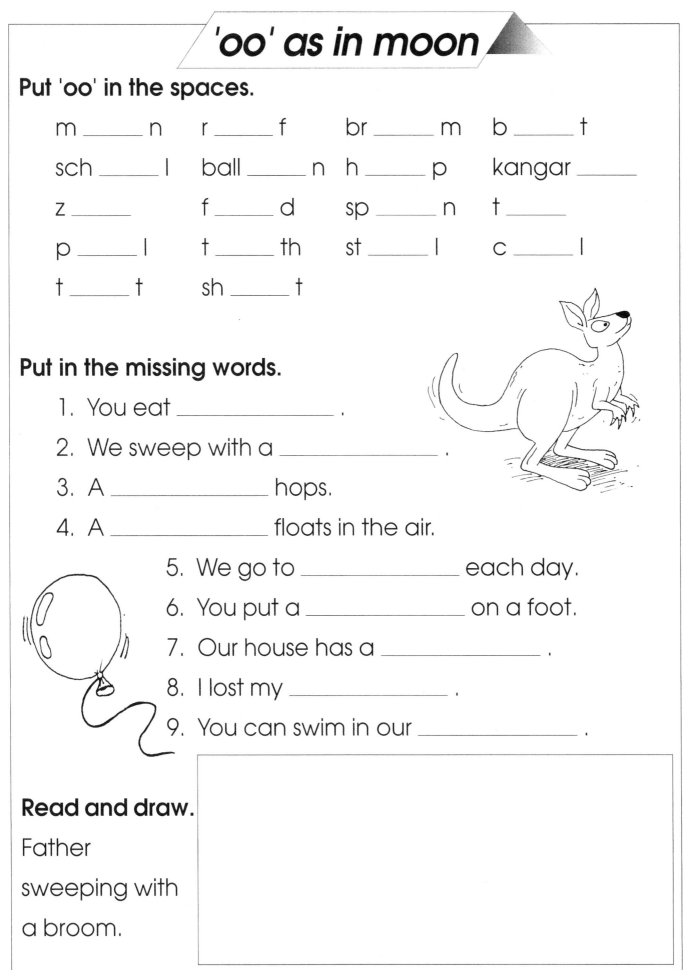

Read and draw.

Father sweeping with a broom.

'ow' as in cow

Put 'ow' in the spaces.

c _____   cl _____ n   t _____ n   h _____

br _____ n   d _____ n   n _____   cr _____ n

dr _____ n   b _____   fr _____ n   fl _____ er

_____ l   gr _____ l   sh _____ er   cr _____ d

t _____ er

Put in the missing words.

1.   I saw an _____ in a tree.

2.   The King has a _____ .

3.   The opposite of up is _____.

4.   We saw a _____ at the circus.

5.   A _____ gives us milk.

Can you find rhyming words?

1. Mrs. Brown went to _____ .

2. The clown is walking upside _____ .

Read and draw.

A clown riding a cow.

A little brown dog is by the cow.

'ay' as in play

Put 'ay' in the spaces.

pl _____   d _____   s _____   st _____

p _____   r _____   h _____   aw _____

cl _____   tr _____   m _____   tod _____

br _____   pr _____   sw _____   cr _____ on

spr _____   w _____   l _____

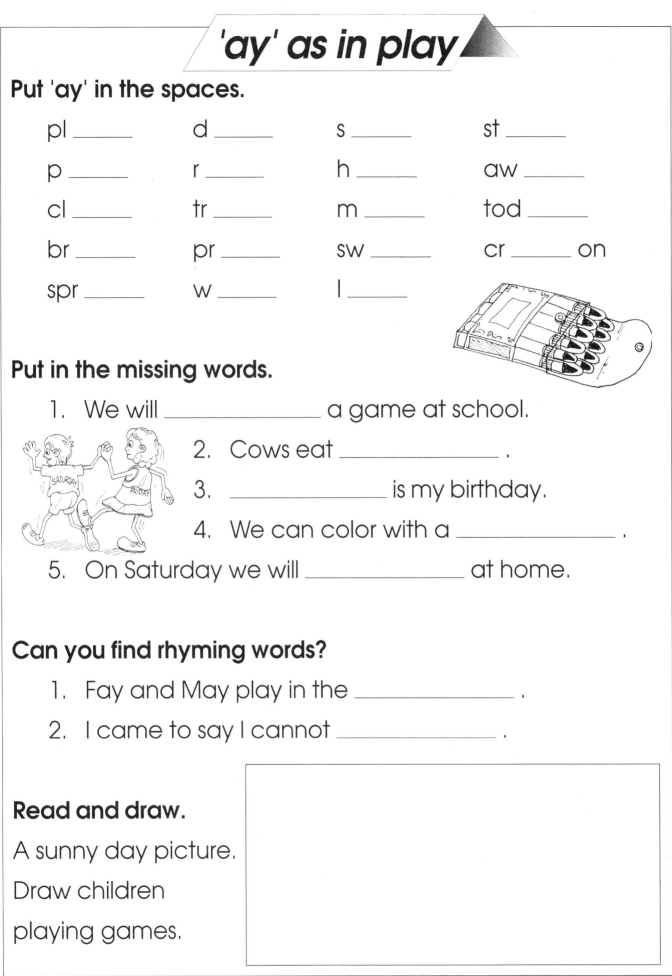

Put in the missing words.

1. We will _____ a game at school.

2. Cows eat _____ .

3. _____ is my birthday.

4. We can color with a _____ .

5. On Saturday we will _____ at home.

Can you find rhyming words?

1. Fay and May play in the _____ .

2. I came to say I cannot _____ .

Read and draw.

A sunny day picture.

Draw children

playing games.

'ai' as in rain

Put 'ai' in the spaces.

r _____ n   tr _____ n   dr _____ n   t _____ l

w _____ t   sn _____ l   n _____ l   p _____ l

p _____ nt   s _____ l   b _____ t   gr _____ n

p _____ n   m _____ n   tr _____ l   p _____ d

l _____ d   ch _____ n   h _____ l   m _____ d

st _____ n

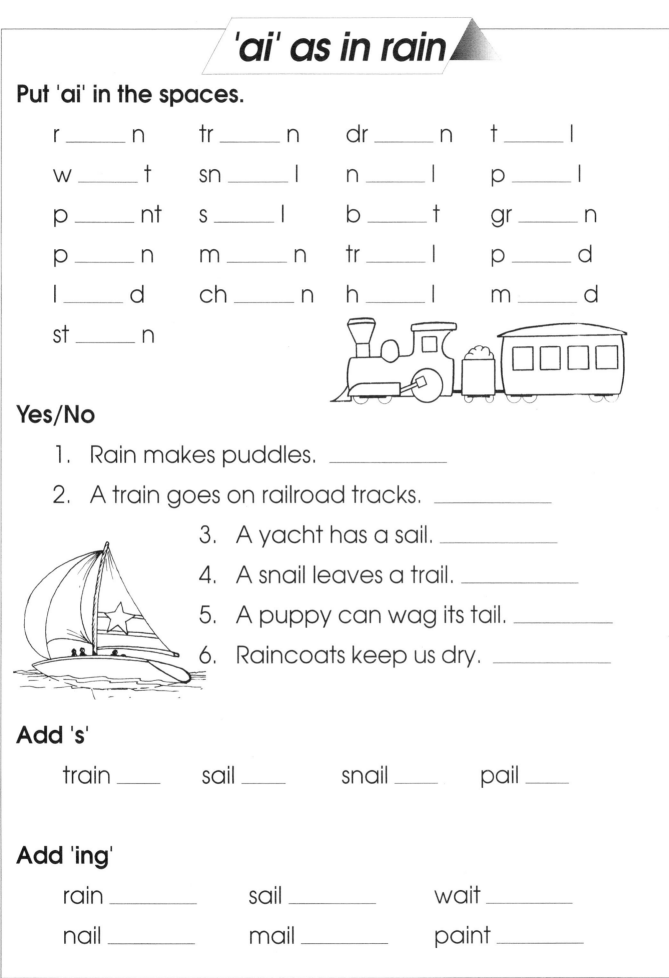

Yes/No

1. Rain makes puddles. _____

2. A train goes on railroad tracks. _____

3. A yacht has a sail. _____

4. A snail leaves a trail. _____

5. A puppy can wag its tail. _____

6. Raincoats keep us dry. _____

Add 's'

train _____   sail _____   snail _____   pail _____

Add 'ing'

rain _____   sail _____   wait _____

nail _____   mail _____   paint _____

'or' as in horse

Put 'or' in the spaces.

doct _____   sh _____ t   st _____ k   f _____

f _____ get   st _____ m   th _____ n   c _____ k

rep _____ t   sp _____ t   h _____ se   f _____ k

rec _____ d   t _____ ch   b _____ n   p _____ k

f _____ ty   f _____ m   t _____ n   m _____ ning

Put in the missing words.

1. I use a _____ to eat my dinner.

2. We got wet in the _____ .

3. In the _____ we get out of bed.

4. Do not _____ your book.

Yes/No

1. Do you like sports? _____

2. Do you like roast pork? _____

3. Do you like storms? _____

4. Do you like horses? _____

Read and draw.

A stormy day.

'oa' as in boat

Put 'oa' in the spaces.

b___t   c___t   g___t   fl___t

m___t   s___p   l___f   thr___t

t___st   r___st   b___st   c___st

cl___k   cr___k   l___d   f___m

m___n   t___d   s___k   c___ch

r___d   ___tmeal

Yes/No

1. A boat will float in the water. _____

2. You can eat oatmeal. _____

3. Frogs and toads croak. _____

4. You can travel in a coach. _____

5. Can you play on the road? _____

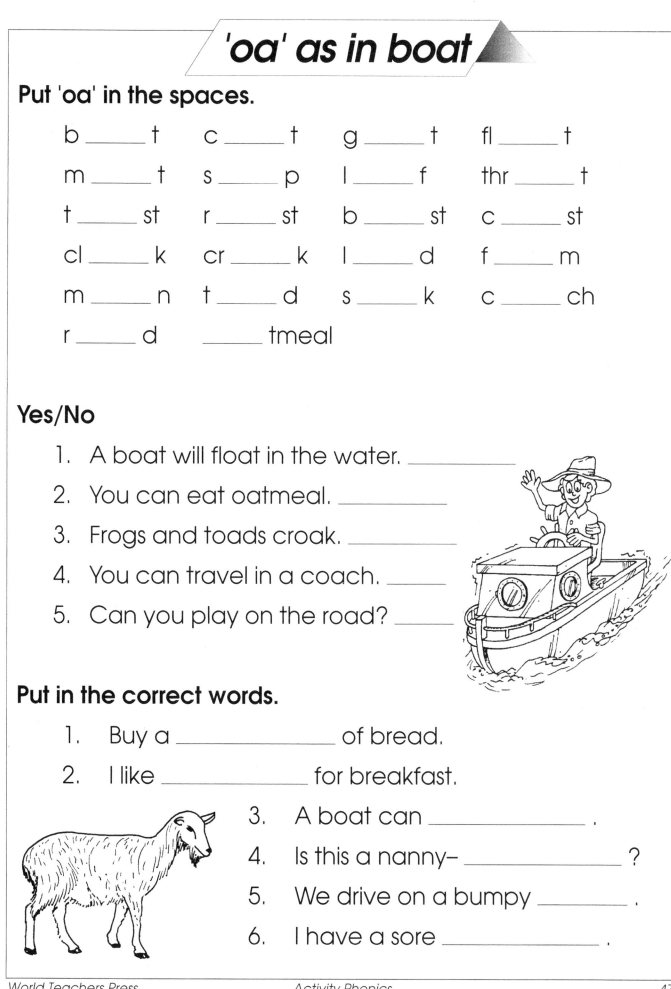

Put in the correct words.

1. Buy a _____ of bread.

2. I like _____ for breakfast.

3. A boat can _____ .

4. Is this a nanny- _____ ?

5. We drive on a bumpy _____ .

6. I have a sore _____ .

'ir' as in bird

Put 'ir' in the spaces.

g _____ l   b _____ d   f _____ st   th _____ d

st _____   sk _____ t   sh _____ t   d _____ t

f _____   ch _____ p   th _____ ty   wh _____ l

th _____ sty   d _____ ty   s _____   tw _____ l

b _____ thday

Yes/No

1. Can a bird fly? _____

2. Are you a girl? _____

3. Do you like birthdays? _____

4. Can you eat dirt? _____

5. Do you have a skirt? _____

6. Do you have a shirt? _____

7. Are you thirty years old? _____

8. Can you whirl and twirl? _____

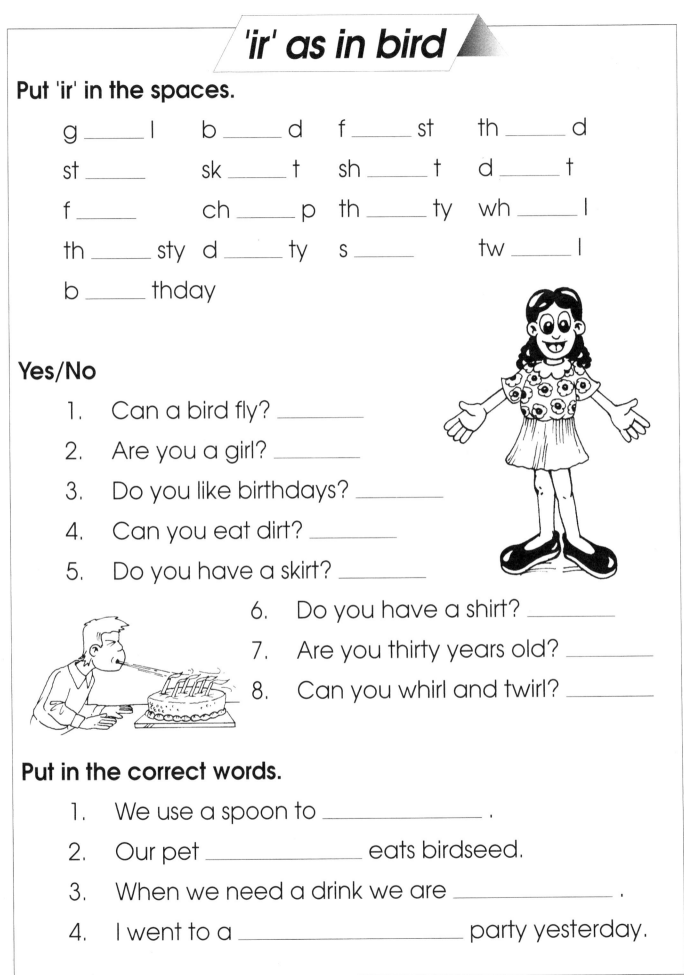

Put in the correct words.

1. We use a spoon to _____ .

2. Our pet _____ eats birdseed.

3. When we need a drink we are _____ .

4. I went to a _____ party yesterday.

'ow' as in bow

Put 'ow' in the spaces.

b _____   fl _____   gr _____   arr _____

l _____   cr _____   gl _____   bl _____

thr _____   sn _____   sh _____   yell _____

              wind _____   bel _____   shad _____

              r _____   marshmall _____

Yes/No

1. Have you seen snow? _____

2. Do you like marshmallows? _____

3. Are you wearing something yellow? _____

4. Can you row a boat? _____

5. Plants grow. _____

6. Have you seen a shadow on the ground? _____

Read and draw.

A snowman has a black hat.

He has a yellow scarf on his neck.

He has a happy face.

'ou' as in house

Put 'ou' in the spaces.

h____se   m____se   cl____d   p____nd

r____nd   s____nd   f____nd   m____th

gr____nd   s____th   al____d   th____sand

____t   sh____t   am____nt   m____ntain

ar____nd   ____tside   ab____t   sh____ting

l____d

Put in the missing words.

1. We must not _____ and run
    _____ in our classroom.

2. We play _____ .

3. The bear went over the _____ .

4. I _____ a penny on the sidewalk.

5. We can buy a _____ of meat.

6. Can you see a _____ in the sky?

7. We planted a tree in the _____ .

Read and draw.

A little mouse
in its house.

'a-e' as in cake

Put 'a-e' in the spaces.

c__k__   m__k__   sn__k__   r__k__

sh__k__   t__k__   b__k__   l__k__

wh__l__   t__l__   l__t__   g__t__

h__t__   d__t__   cr__t__   pl__t__

Put in the missing words.

1. We will _____ up the leaves.

2. Please shut the _____ .

3. Mother will _____ a _____ .

4. Put the cake on the _____ .

5. Do not be _____ for school.

6. Don't forget to _____ your reading book.

What am I? Draw me.

I am very big.

I swim in the sea.

I am a _____ .

Draw a snake by a rake.

'a-e' as in cake

Put 'a-e' in the spaces.

m__d__   g__v__   c__v__   s__v__

sh__v__   br__v__   n__m__   c__m__

g__m__   c__p__   l__n__

s__f__   sh__d__   sp__d__

What am I? Draw me.

I am found in the shed.

You dig with me.

I am a _____ .

How do I help? Draw me.

I am a tree.

I give people _____ .

Draw a safe place to play.

Name a game you like to play. _____

'i-e' as in kite

Put 'i-e' in the spaces.

k__t__   b__t__   s__t__   outs__d__

b__k__   h__k__   f__v__   h__v__

r__p__   w__p__   f__n__   sh__n__

d__c__   p__l__   l__k__   wh__t__

m__n__   s__d__   h__d__   dr__v__

n__n__   __c__   l__n__   r__d__

l__f__   t__m__   sl__d__   sm__l__

Yes/No

1. Can you ride a bike? _____

2. Can a baby smile? _____

3. Can you tell the time? _____

4. Do you like ice cream? _____

5. Can Dad drive a car? _____

6. Do you have a fishing line? _____

Read and draw.

Five children playing in the park. They are all flying kites.

'o-e' as in bone

Put 'o-e' in the spaces.

b__n__   c__n__   st__n__   n__t__

h__m__   sp__k__   j__k__   r__p__

h__p__   w__k__   r__d__   br__k__

r__s__   h__s__   n__s__   teleph__n__

Put in the correct words.

1. We smell with our _____ .

2. It is fun to skip with a _____ .

3. I _____ my bike home.

4. The dog hid his _____ .

5. Do not throw a _____ .

6. The stone _____ the window.

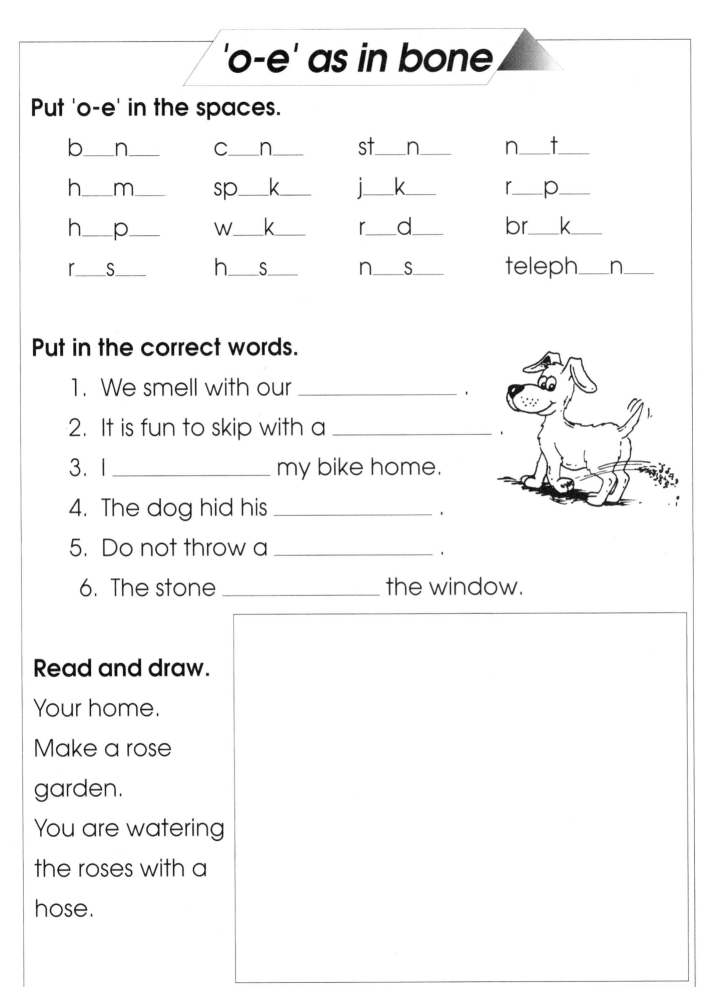

Read and draw.

Your home.

Make a rose garden.

You are watering the roses with a hose.

'scr' as in screw

Put 'scr' in the spaces.

_____ew	_____een	_____ibble
_____amble	_____ub	_____oll
_____eam	_____ape	_____ap
_____ubbing	_____atch	_____ewdriver
_____apbook		

Put in the correct words.

1. Use the _____ to fix the door.
2. The television has a _____ .
3. Do not _____ on the paper.
4. We have to _____ the floor.
5. A cat can _____ .

Yes/No

1. Do you like scrambled eggs? _____
2. Do you scribble? _____
3. Do you have a scrapbook? _____
4. Do you scrub your nails? _____
5. Does your television have a screen? _____
6. Does a tiger scratch? _____

'spl' as in splash

Put 'spl' in the spaces.

_____ash   _____int   _____it   _____inter

_____ice   _____its   _____atter

_____endid   _____ashed

Put in the missing words.

1. Baby _____ in the bath tub.

2. She _____ the candy bar into two pieces.

3. We had a _____ meal.

4. The doctor put a _____ on my arm.

5. Baby _____ed us with water.

Yes/No

1. Have you had a splinter? _____

2. Do you splash when you swim? _____

3. Can you do the splits? _____

Read and draw.

A swimming pool.

Draw children

splashing in the pool.

'str' as in string

Put 'str' in the spaces.

_____ing	_____ap	_____eam
_____ainer	_____etch	_____and
_____ain	_____aw	_____anger
_____ay	_____eet	_____ipe
_____oll	_____ong	_____uggle
_____aight	_____awberry	

Yes/No

1. Can a cat stretch? _____
2. A tiger has stripes. _____
3. Should you talk to strangers? _____
4. A line is straight. _____
5. Can you eat a strawberry? _____
6. Do you live on a street? _____

Draw a straight line.

Read and draw.

Your street.

Put your house

on the street.

'thr' as in three

Put 'thr' in the spaces.

_____ee   _____ow   _____oat

_____ead   _____ew   _____one

_____ough   _____own   _____ob

Put in the missing words.

1. I have a sore _____ .

2. I can _____ a needle.

3. The Queen sits on a _____ .

4. The lion went _____ the hoop.

5. The teacher _____ the ball.

6. We can _____ a beanbag.

7. The juggler can juggle _____ balls.

Read and draw.

Three friends going through hoops.

'spr' as in spring

Put 'spr' in the spaces.

_____ing   _____ig   _____ead

_____inkler   _____ay   _____inkle

_____outs   _____ain   _____ee

_____int   _____out

Put in the missing words.

1. We planted some _____ .

2. In _____ we see many pretty flowers.

3. All our seeds are beginning to _____ .

4. We watered the lawn with the _____ .

5. The runner will _____ .

6. First _____ the bread with butter then _____ on the sugar.

7. I have a new bed_____ on my bed.

Read and draw.

A spring day.

Make sure you put in baby animals and spring flowers.

'squ' as in squirrel

Put 'squ' in the spaces.

_____irrel	_____id	_____ash
_____are	_____eeze	_____ad
_____eak	_____eal	_____irm
_____iggle	_____int	_____irt

Put in the missing words.

1. A _____ eats nuts.

2. A _____ lives in the sea.

3. An elephant can _____ water.

4. A mouse can _____ .

5. A _____ has four sides.

6. We _____ a lemon to make a drink.

Read and draw.

Two squirrels in a tree.

They are eating nuts.

An elephant
squirting water.

About the Author

Betty Pollard, Bunbury, Western Australia.
Betty has many years of teaching experience and specializes in the elementary grades. Her titles focus on the phonics area of language development and present a very structured, easy-to-follow approach. The success of her phonics books throughout the world has been outstanding and reflects the need in classrooms for materials that are developmental in nature and structured in format.